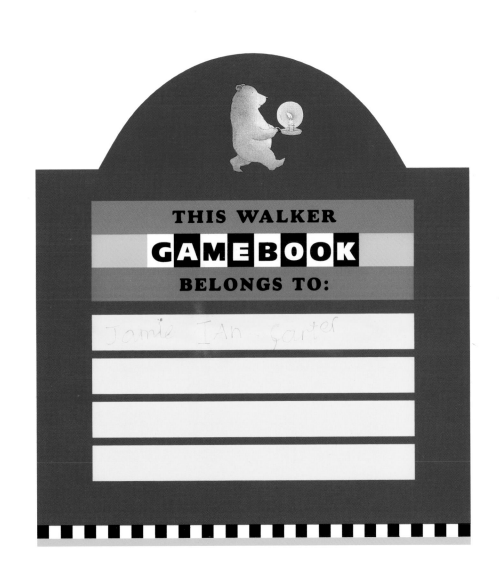

THIS WALKER
**GAMEBOOK**
BELONGS TO:

Jamie IAn Carter

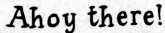

# Ahoy there!

I'm Mam Spamme - terror of the Seven Seas! I'm about to tell you the tale of how we won the treasure of Captain Blood and defeated Red Roger, the wicked Governor of Chutney Island. And to make sure you don't fall asleep while I'm telling it, I'm going to give you puzzles to solve as you go along, so keep your eyes peeled and your wits sharp. First of all, meet the Heroes and Villains.

**MAM SPAMME**
Me. The Heroine!

**SAM SPAMME**
My son. The greediest
pirate afloat.

**BLACK DOG**
The bravest,
most intelligent
dog in this story.

# The
# Heroic
# Spammes

**THE
SPOTTED DOG**
Our ship.

**THE RAT CREW**
Brave, reckless
and a bit unlucky.

# The LOST TREASURE of CAPTAIN BLOOD

*How the infamous Spammes escaped the jaws of death and won a vast and glorious fortune.*

**RED ROGER**
The Governor of
Chutney Island.

## The Dastardly Villains

**NELSON**
The cruellest cat
ever to swing a
cutlass.

Written by
## Jonathan Stroud

Illustrated by
## Cathy Gale

To N. and G. with love.
**J.S.**
To Granny Cooper, the
original Mam Spamme.
**C.G.**

First published 1996
by Walker Books Ltd
87 Vauxhall Walk
London SE11 5HJ

This edition published 1997

2 4 6 8 10 9 7 5 3 1

Text © 1996 Jonathan Stroud
Illustrations © 1996 Cathy Gale

This book has been typeset in
Alpha Regular and Beta Regular

Printed in Hong Kong

British Library Cataloguing
in Publication Data
A catalogue record for this book
is available from the British Library.

ISBN 0-7445-5268-0

## WALKER BOOKS
### AND SUBSIDIARIES
LONDON • BOSTON • SYDNEY

## BILL BLOOD CAPTURED!

Bill Blood, the famous pirate, was finally captured last night by our Governor Red Roger and his fearless henchpuss, Nelson the cat. They caught him napping in his cottage on Dead Man's Head and put him in the dungeon of DEVIL'S FORTRESS. He will be taken next week to PIRATES' LEAP and hanged.

## TREASURE!

Bill Blood is said to have hidden a huge hoard of treasure somewhere here on CHUTNEY ISLAND. No one knows where it is. He has given his treasure map to his old shipmate, Mam Spamme, for safe-keeping.

Red Roger in Bill Blood's parlour. Blood's belongings were auctioned off this morning.

Fearless henchpuss, Nelson.

## ROGER SETS SAIL!

Roger set sail before breakfast, intending to capture his old enemies, the Spammes. He will then use the map to find the treasure and return it to its rightful owners.

Roger's ship, the Semolina.

## SPY SETS OUT!

Roger has sent his top spy to follow the Spammes. He will keep well hidden and send messages to Roger using Fred the carrier pigeon.

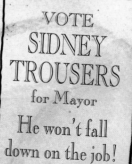
You now have all the information you need to follow the story. Just look out for the puzzles in the black flags and solve them as you go. Now buckle your cutlasses and turn the page.

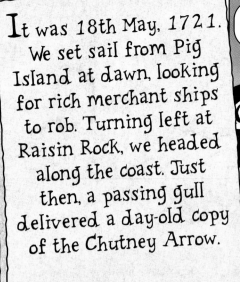

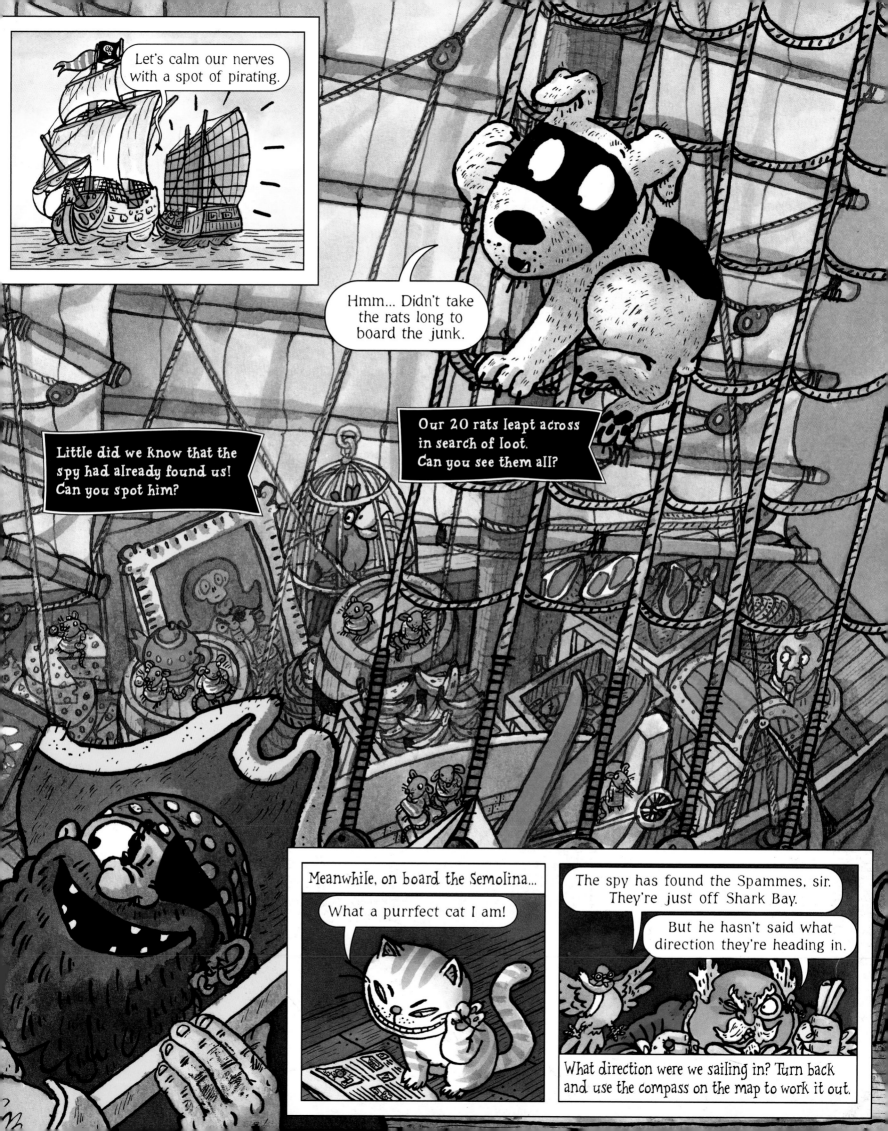

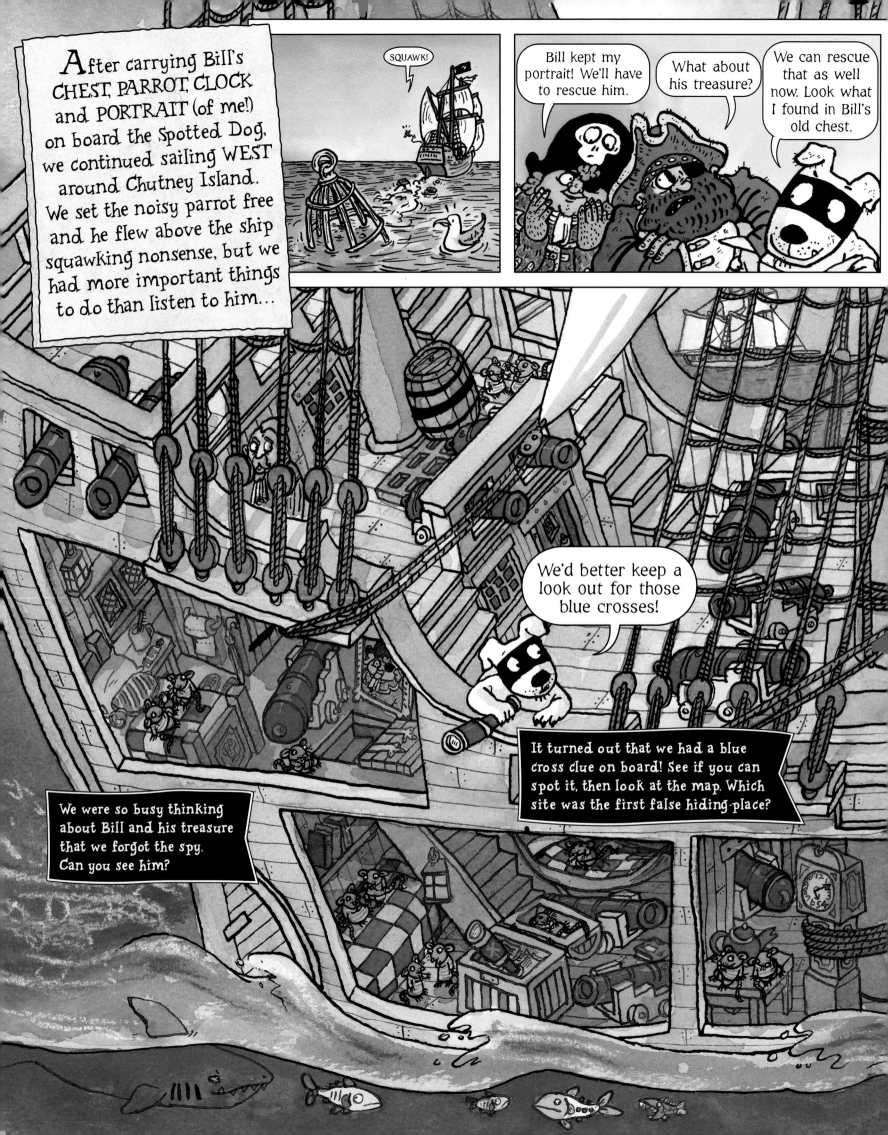

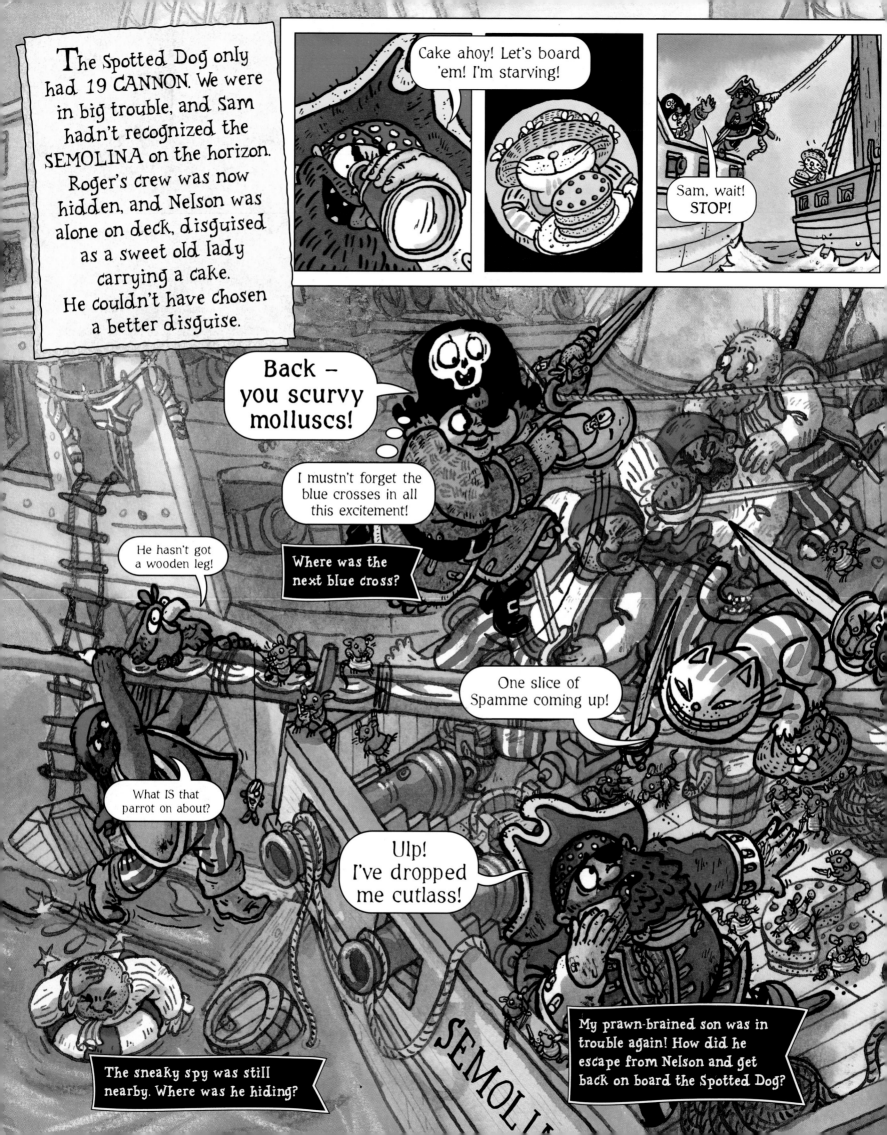

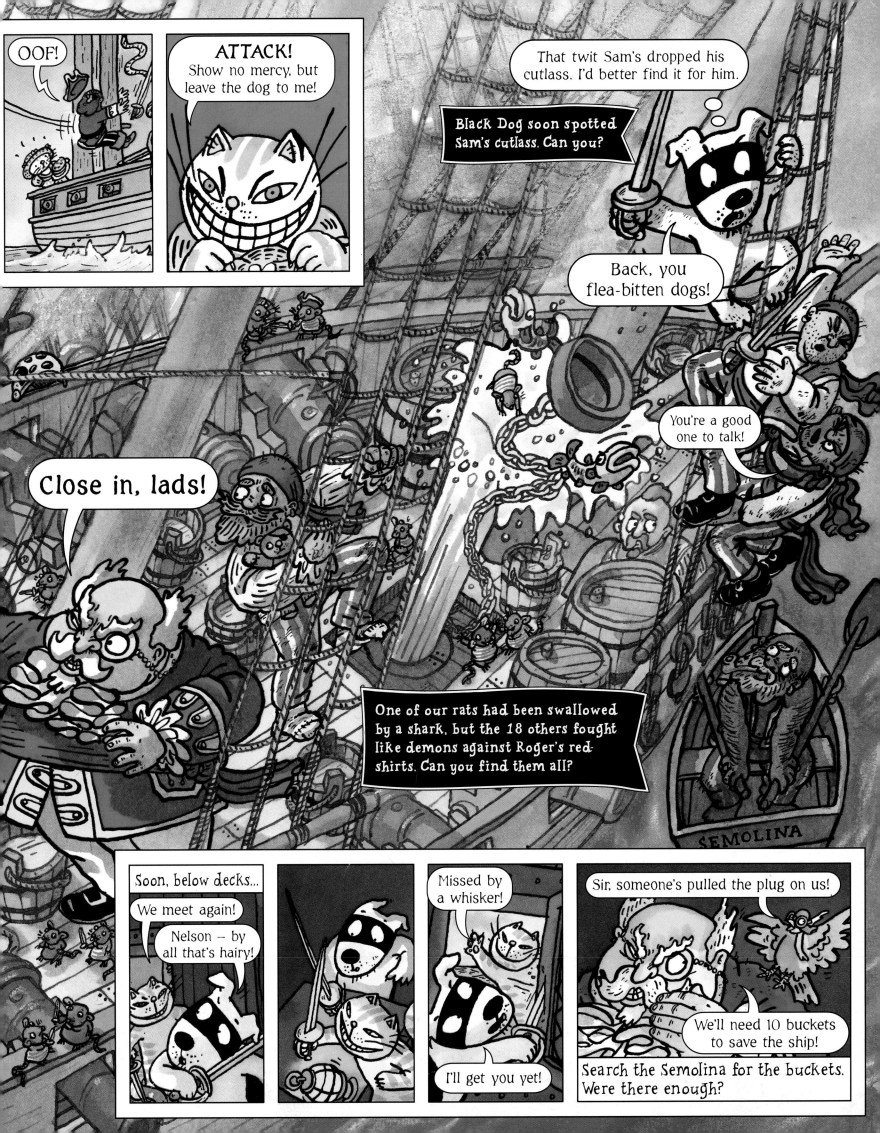

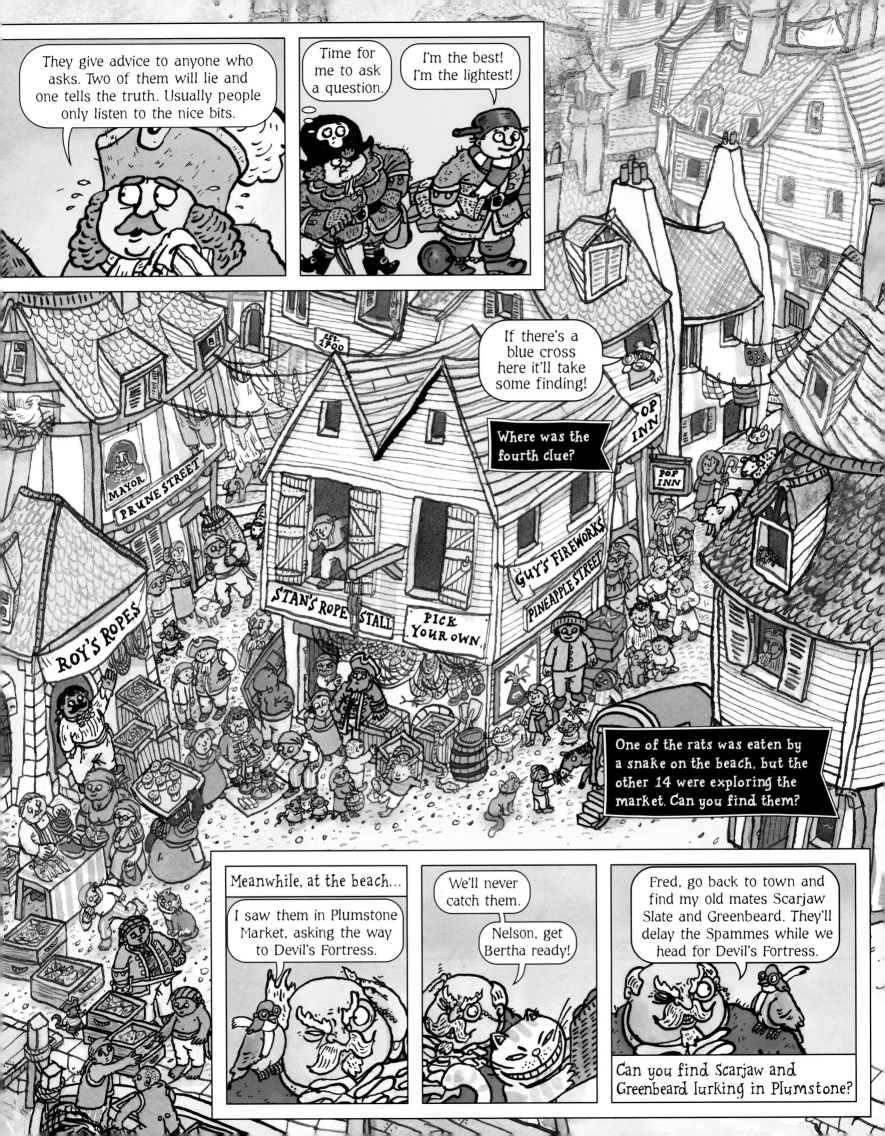

Where's the rope?

Sam's got it!

No. I haven't! I cleverly dropped it before I fell in.

Sam, stop lounging about down there! Come out!

I can't!

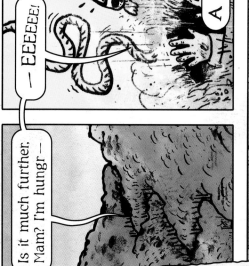

— EEEEEE!

A trap!

Is it much further, Mam? I'm hungr—

When Sam got back from ROY'S ROPE STORE we set off down PINEAPPLE STREET (the street without a poster). Scarjaw and Greenbeard watched us from the FISH STALL; they knew we were heading for a trap they had dug long ago to catch unwary travellers!

Only 10 rats escaped the Plumstone cats. Can you spot them all?

He hasn't got a patch.

Which was the nearest branch safe enough to tie the rope to?

Then we'll need to tie it to a branch so that Sam can climb up.

First we need to find the rope.

Where had the rope landed?

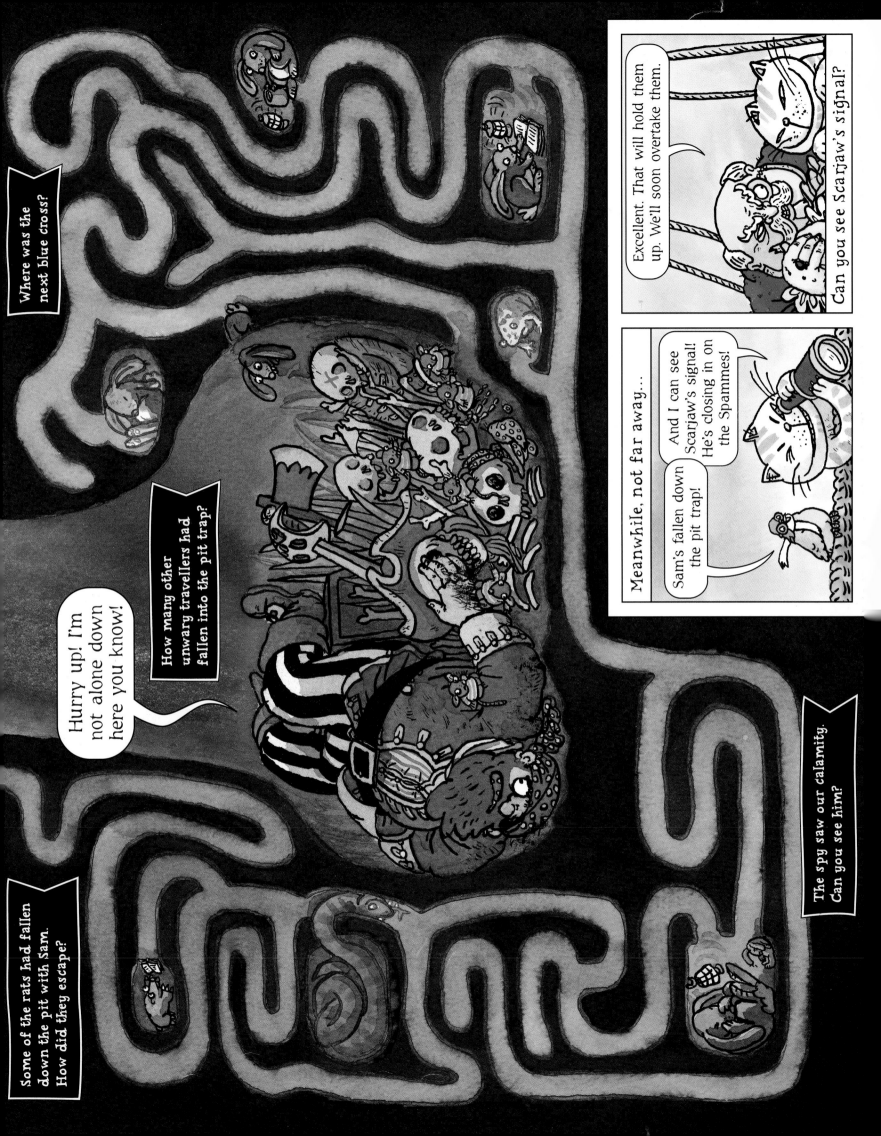

We found the rope in the trees and tied it to the branch with a BUTTERFLY on it. Sam said goodbye to the 5 SKELETONS and climbed out - but our troubles had only just begun! Scarjaw had signalled to Roger with his SPOTTED HANDKERCHIEF and was preparing to attack.

We were lost in the deepest, darkest bit of jungle, but we escaped by using our wits. Follow each of my JUNGLE SURVIVAL TIPS in turn and work out how we escaped without retracing our steps.

# MAM'S JUNGLE SURVIVAL TIPS

1. Cross at the log bridges but beware: red spruce trunks are rotten - avoid them!

2. Now find some flowers.

3. Take them to the wild bees and exchange them for some honey.

4. Head for the bear - avoid the fire termites...

and the ferocious jaguar.

5. Offer the honey to the bear and slip past.

6. Find the place with 2 boats tied up together. Alligators overturn boats with more than 2 passengers.

7. Float downstream to Devil's Fortress, avoiding all the whirlpools.

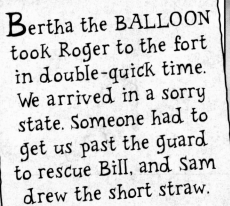

Nelson made his choice...

WHOOPS! Wrong one!

Ha-harr!

CLANG!

Caught in their own trap!

Nothing can stop us n-eh?

MAM!

MAM!

MAM!

Mam, you old walrus!

Mam! Let me out!

Oh, no! They're all so dirty and ugly, any one of them could be Bill!

He hasn't got a red hat!

Three rats were raiding the kitchen, but 4 were exploring the dungeon. Can you find them?

Wait! The parrot knows the answer! He's been telling us all along!

The parrot's squawks were not nonsense after all! Look back at all his clues and work out which prisoner was the real Bill Blood. Can you pick out the spy as well?

WAIT! Before you turn over, find the eighth and last blue cross clue! When you've found and solved it, you should have just one possible treasure site left on your map! If you think you know where it is, read on!

Suddenly, everything was going right! If Nelson had cut the rope tied to the YELLOW lever, we would have been flatter than flatfish. But he'd cut the BROWN one and the villains were trapped. While Sam tied them up, the parrot's clues led us straight to CELL 9! I broke the door down and Bill was free! Now we had to escape.

Look what I've found!

TO BEACH

Ooof!

One escape later...

Hurrah! We're out! Now for Bill's treasure!

Clever of you to hide it near the dreaded gallows — the last place any pirate would want to look!

You're right. The chest's in one of those caves...

Trouble is, I can't remember which. And I left deadly spiders in the others. We'll have to use the sum I invented to remind me.

There was nothing for it but to solve Bill's sum. We found the right cave, eventually. Can you?

BILL'S SUM

Take the number of PIRATE BOOTS lying on the beach.

Add the number of CARRION CROWS.

Take away the number of SKULLS scattered on the cliffs.

The answer will be the same as the number of SWORDS outside the TREASURE CAVE.

Even after Roger's capture, his spy couldn't get out of the habit of watching us! Can you spot him?